The Caged Bird

Written by
CLAIRE KELLY

Illustrated by
MIKE ROOTH

D1571302

This story is set in Burma at the end of the last century. Each chapter ends with a non-fiction page that gives more information about real people's lives and actual events at that time.

OXFORD
UNIVERSITY PRESS

SERAWOOT

AUNG SAN SUU KYI

SIPAN

NOI

REAL PEOPLE IN HISTORY

AUNG SAN SUU KYI (born 1945): The Burmese freedom fighter who leads from the prison of her own home.

FICTIONAL CHARACTERS

SERAWOOT: A young boy whose parents have been captured by the government.

SIPAN: Serawoot's grandfather. He is a professor who disagrees with the government.

NOI: A young rebel who helps his friends when they most need it.

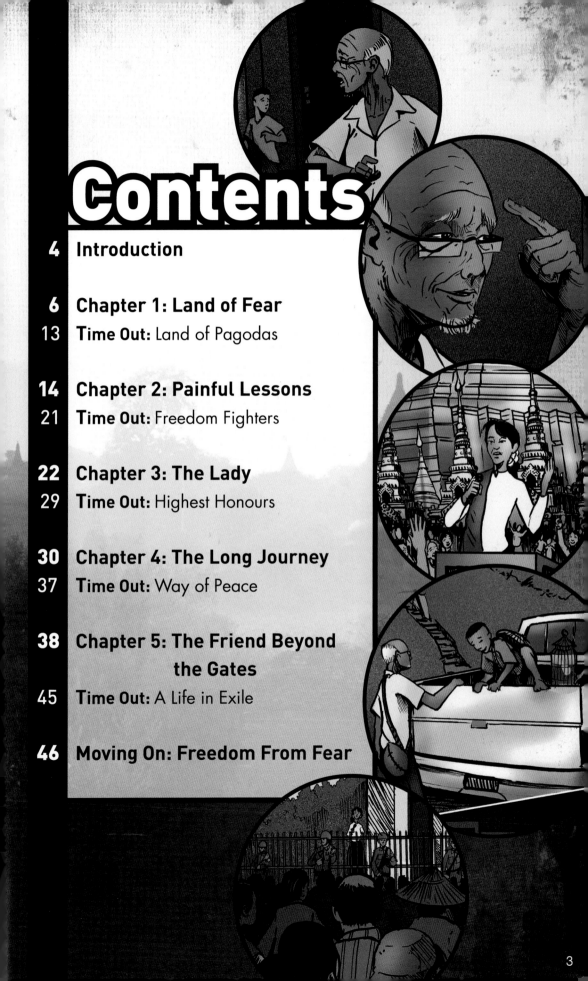

Contents

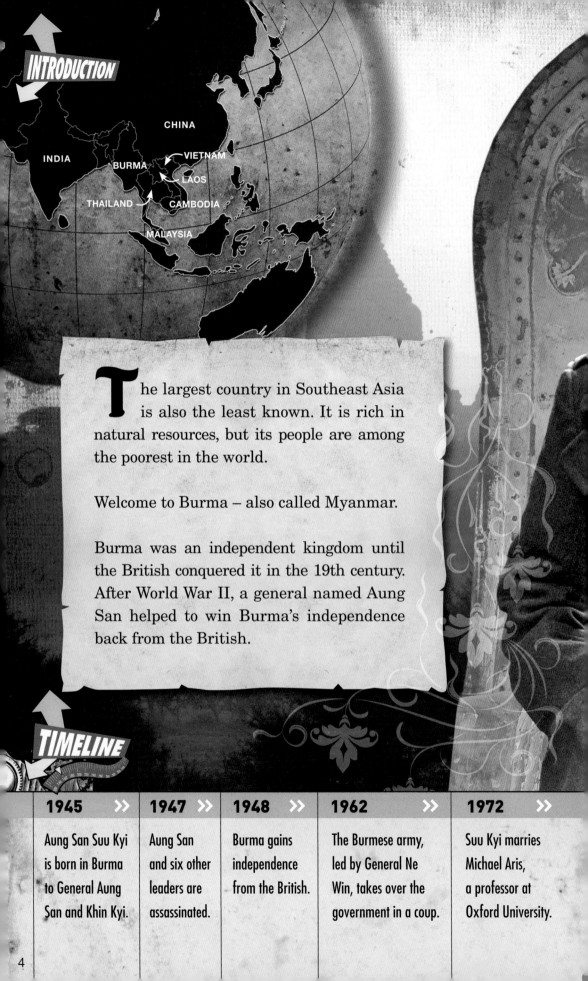

CHINA

INDIA

BURMA

VIETNAM

LAOS

THAILAND

CAMBODIA

MALAYSIA

The largest country in Southeast Asia is also the least known. It is rich in natural resources, but its people are among the poorest in the world.

Welcome to Burma – also called Myanmar.

Burma was an independent kingdom until the British conquered it in the 19th century. After World War II, a general named Aung San helped to win Burma's independence back from the British.

TIMELINE

1945 >>	1947 >>	1948 >>	1962 >>	1972 >>
Aung San Suu Kyi is born in Burma to General Aung San and Khin Kyi.	Aung San and six other leaders are assassinated.	Burma gains independence from the British.	The Burmese army, led by General Ne Win, takes over the government in a coup.	Suu Kyi marries Michael Aris, a professor at Oxford University.

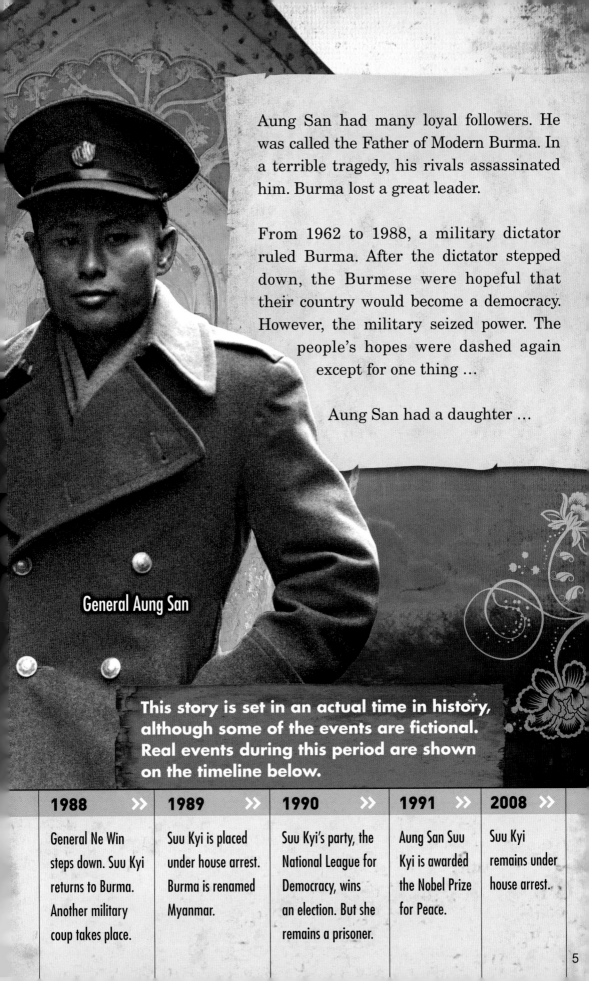

Aung San had many loyal followers. He was called the Father of Modern Burma. In a terrible tragedy, his rivals assassinated him. Burma lost a great leader.

From 1962 to 1988, a military dictator ruled Burma. After the dictator stepped down, the Burmese were hopeful that their country would become a democracy. However, the military seized power. The people's hopes were dashed again except for one thing …

Aung San had a daughter …

General Aung San

This story is set in an actual time in history, although some of the events are fictional. Real events during this period are shown on the timeline below.

1988 >>	1989 >>	1990 >>	1991 >>	2008 >>
General Ne Win steps down. Suu Kyi returns to Burma. Another military coup takes place.	Suu Kyi is placed under house arrest. Burma is renamed Myanmar.	Suu Kyi's party, the National League for Democracy, wins an election. But she remains a prisoner.	Aung San Suu Kyi is awarded the Nobel Prize for Peace.	Suu Kyi remains under house arrest.

JULY 2003: A RAINY DAY IN A SMALL VILLAGE IN SOUTHEAST BURMA NEAR THE THAI BORDER.

I HATE THIS RAIN!

GET USED TO IT, SERAWOOT. THIS IS THE MONSOON SEASON.

CHEER UP, MY BOY.

SUDDENLY, AN ANNOUNCEMENT COMES OVER THE RADIO.

THE GOVERNMENT WILL NOT RELEASE ANY POLITICAL PRISONERS FOR MARTYRS' DAY THIS YEAR.

SERAWOOT TELLS HIS GRANDFATHER WHAT HAPPENED.

CHIEP WAS NOT RIGHT TO TAKE THE BOOK, BUT YOU SHOULD NOT HAVE FOUGHT WITH HIM.

I KNOW, GRANDFATHER. I'M SORRY.

VIOLENCE IS NOT THE ANSWER, SERAWOOT.

HE SAW ALL OUR BOOKS, AND THE PHOTO OF 'THE LADY'?

YES, GRANDFATHER. I COULD NOT STOP HIM.

THAT'S NOT GOOD.

SIPAN PUTS HIS BOOKS IN A PILE ON THE FLOOR.

WHAT ARE YOU DOING?

WE'LL GET INTO TROUBLE FOR HAVING THESE BOOKS, SERAWOOT.

WE MUST BURN THEM. EVERY LAST ONE!

LAND OF PAGODAS

Burma is a land of rugged mountains and fertile river plains. It is rich in oil, precious gems and valuable woods such as teak. However, Burma is a poor and isolated country.

The ancient kings of Burma were, like many Burmese today, devout Buddhists. They built thousands of pagodas to show their faith. These pagodas can still be seen all over the country.

The people of Burma are of many different ethnic groups. The largest groups are the Burmese, the Shan and the Karen. The Karen people have fought for their independence for many years.

In 1989, the government of Burma changed the country's name to Myanmar. Many people who disagree with their rule still call the country by its old name.

Burmese pagodas (temples)

15

FREEDOM FIGHTERS

Some people are put in prison not for their crimes but for what they believe in. Often, these people speak out against injustice or they disagree with their country's government. Because they are jailed for their sense of right and wrong, they are called 'prisoners of conscience'.

Aung San Suu Kyi is a prisoner of conscience. There are others like her around the world.

Nelson Mandela (born 1918): South Africa

He spent 26 years in prison for protesting against South Africa's system of racial segregation. After his release, he was elected president of South Africa.

Andrei Sakharov (1921–1989): Former Soviet Union

He was a scientist who helped develop nuclear weapons. He later spoke out against such weapons and in favour of human rights. He was sent away to a remote city for six years.

Phuntsog Nyidron (born 1968): Tibet

She is a Tibetan nun who was arrested for supporting Tibet's independence from China. She spent 15 years in jail and was released in 2004.

SIPAN TELLS THE STORY OF THE LADY IN THE PORTRAIT.

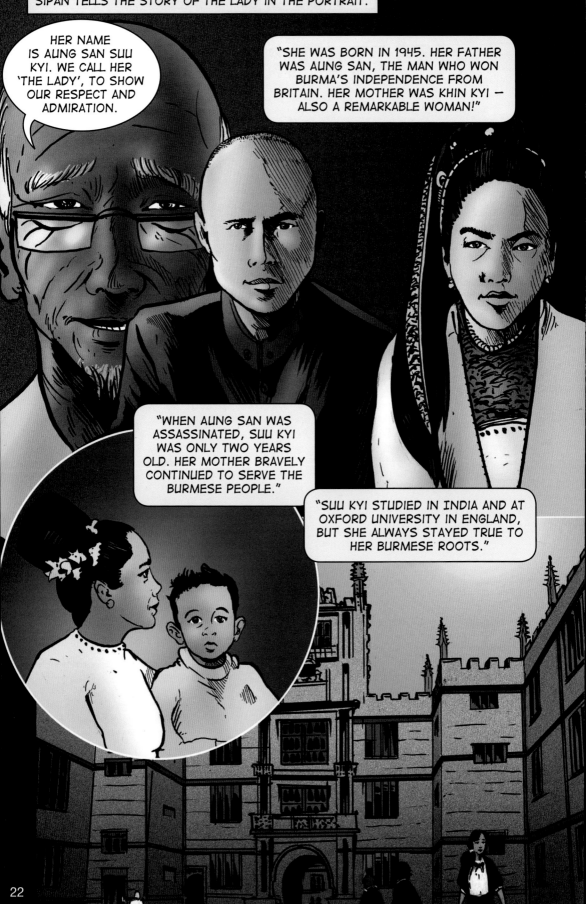

HER NAME IS AUNG SAN SUU KYI. WE CALL HER 'THE LADY', TO SHOW OUR RESPECT AND ADMIRATION.

"SHE WAS BORN IN 1945. HER FATHER WAS AUNG SAN, THE MAN WHO WON BURMA'S INDEPENDENCE FROM BRITAIN. HER MOTHER WAS KHIN KYI — ALSO A REMARKABLE WOMAN!"

"WHEN AUNG SAN WAS ASSASSINATED, SUU KYI WAS ONLY TWO YEARS OLD. HER MOTHER BRAVELY CONTINUED TO SERVE THE BURMESE PEOPLE."

"SUU KYI STUDIED IN INDIA AND AT OXFORD UNIVERSITY IN ENGLAND, BUT SHE ALWAYS STAYED TRUE TO HER BURMESE ROOTS."

"SUU, AS HER FRIENDS CALL HER, GREW UP TO BE A BEAUTIFUL AND SERIOUS YOUNG LADY. SHE FELL IN LOVE WITH MICHAEL ARIS, AN ENGLISHMAN. THEY MARRIED IN 1972 AND LIVED IN ENGLAND."

"WHEN SUU KYI'S MOTHER FELL ILL IN 1988, SUU KYI RUSHED FROM ENGLAND TO BE WITH HER."

AT THIS TIME, THE COUNTRY WAS IN TURMOIL.

GENERAL NE WIN, THE MAN WHO HAD RULED BURMA HARSHLY FOR 26 YEARS, STEPPED DOWN.

"OUR PEOPLE ROSE UP, DEMANDING CHANGE AND A FAIR GOVERNMENT."

"SUU KYI KNEW WHAT WAS EXPECTED OF HER. HER FAMILY WAS IN ENGLAND, BUT HER DESTINY LAY WITH BURMA."

"ON 26 AUGUST 1988, SUU KYI SPOKE TO A CROWD OF HALF A MILLION PEOPLE, IN FRONT OF THE SHWEDAGON PAGODA — A SYMBOL OF OUR COUNTRY AND OUR MOST SACRED BUDDHIST TEMPLE."

THE BURMESE PEOPLE MUST CHOOSE THEIR OWN GOVERNMENT.

"SUU KYI WAS CHOSEN TO LEAD A NEW PARTY CALLED THE NATIONAL LEAGUE FOR DEMOCRACY. PEOPLE IN BURMA SAW IN HER THE HOPE FOR A NEW FUTURE."

FOR THIS REASON, OUR MILITARY LEADERS WERE VERY AFRAID OF HER.

THEY ALMOST KILLED HER.

HOW?

HIGHEST HONOURS

Alfred Nobel was a Swedish scientist. He became very famous and rich from his invention of dynamite. Nobel did not want to be remembered for inventing an explosive substance. He left his wealth to a good cause. He created Nobel Prizes to reward high achievements and people's work for humanity.

The Nobel Prizes are given out every year in the fields of physics, chemistry, medicine, economics, literature and peace. The Peace Prize is given to those who make outstanding contributions to world peace.

Aung San Suu Kyi won the Nobel Peace Prize in 1991. She was under house arrest at the time. Her teenage sons, Alexander and Kim, received the prize on her behalf.

Alfred Nobel

Aung San Suu Kyi sits during an interview in front of a portrait of her father, General Aung San.

DURING THE JOURNEY, SERAWOOT SEES THAT BURMA IS EVEN MORE BEAUTIFUL THAN HE HAD IMAGINED.

WAY OF PEACE

TIME OUT!

> In a gentle way, you can shake the world.
> — Mahatma Gandhi

Throughout history, people have often tried to change society by fighting one another. There are those, however, who reject fighting as a way to bring about change. These people support non-violent means instead, such as vigils, sit-ins and peaceful demonstrations. They are all leaders who have won widespread support and admiration.

Gandhi was the man who won India's independence from Britain. He taught that to achieve peace, one must be peaceful.

Martin Luther King Jr led the civil rights movement in the United States. He also insisted on non-violence.

the Dalai Lama is the spiritual leader of the Tibetan people.

ON THE WAY TO SEE AUNG SAN SUU KYI ...

IS THIS THE WAY TO THE LADY'S HOUSE, GRANDFATHER?

SSH! SERAWOOT — I MEAN, HOM — BE CAREFUL. WE MIGHT BE OVERHEARD.

SOMEONE MIGHT RECOGNISE ME. WE COULD BE IN DANGER.

YES, GRANDFATHER.

NO ONE WILL RECOGNISE YOU IF YOU WEAR YOUR HAT!

YOU'RE RIGHT. NOW I DON'T LOOK LIKE A PROFESSOR.

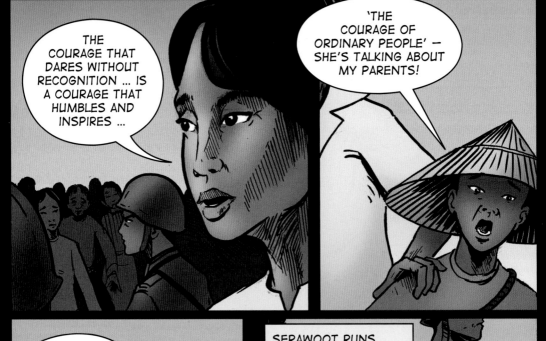

THE COURAGE THAT DARES WITHOUT RECOGNITION ... IS A COURAGE THAT HUMBLES AND INSPIRES ...

'THE COURAGE OF ORDINARY PEOPLE' — SHE'S TALKING ABOUT MY PARENTS!

I THINK SHE'S TALKING TO ME! I MUST GO NEARER!

SERAWOOT!

SERAWOOT RUNS TOWARDS THE FENCE.

HE DARTS PAST THE POLICE GUARDS!

43

Refugees walk in the Mae Hla camp near the Burmese border in Mae Hla, Thailand.

A Life in Exile

Hundreds of thousands of people have fled Burma to escape the military government's harsh rule. Many of these people are from different ethnic groups. The government prevents them from practising their culture or religion.

These people have fled to neighbouring countries such as Thailand, Bangladesh, India, Malaysia and China. Some of them are recognised as refugees and live in camps set up by their host countries. Others have no legal status in these countries and live in fear of arrest.

Life is very hard for these exiles. As a Burmese refugee in Malaysia told some aid workers, "I have very little hope. All I can do is pray that somehow these difficult times will pass."

Freedom From Fear

> The only real prison is fear, and the only real freedom is freedom from fear.
>
> – Aung San Suu Kyi

In 1997, Aung San Suu Kyi's husband, Michael Aris, learned that he had cancer. He pleaded with the government of Myanmar to let him visit Suu Kyi in Rangoon. They refused. He passed away in 1999 without seeing his wife again.

As of 2008, Suu Kyi still lives as a prisoner in her own home. Many world leaders have called on the government of Myanmar to release her and to recognise the 1990 election results that should have swept her into power. The struggle continues.

Aung San Suu Kyi during a press conference in 2002

The people of Burma live in poverty and misery because of their government. But Suu Kyi's courageous example has given them hope – and inspiration.

A young woman named Su Su Nway is leading the next generation of freedom fighters in Burma. She made headlines around the world by fighting against forced labour, the practice of making people work against their will. Su Su Nway spent eight months in jail, but it didn't break her spirit. On her release, she said, "I take my prison uniform with me because I know that I will have to come back to jail until Burma gets democracy."

Statue of Buddha

INDEX

GLOSSARY

assassinate – to kill an important person deliberately, especially for political reasons

corrupt – dishonest

democracy – government of a country by representatives elected by the people of that country

dictator – a ruler who has unlimited power and cannot be voted out

forbidden – to not be allowed to do something

freedom fighter – someone prepared to use violence in order to achieve freedom

martyr – a person who is killed or made to suffer because of his or her beliefs

monsoon – a strong wind over and near the Indian Ocean which brings heavy rain in the summer

refugee – a person who has had to leave his/her home or country

sacrifice – to give up something precious

turmoil – wild confusion

vigil – to stay awake to pray, often as part of a protest